The
Cosmic Ordering
Wish Book
2008

The
Cosmic Ordering
Wish Book
2008

by
Barbel Mohr
and Pierre Franckh

HAY HOUSE

Australia • Canada • Hong Kong
South Africa • United Kingdom • United States

First published and distributed in the United Kingdom by:
Hay House UK Ltd, 292B Kensal Rd, London W10 5BE.
Tel.: (44) 20 8962 1230; Fax: (44) 20 8962 1239. www.hayhouse.co.uk

Published and distributed in the United States of America by:
Hay House, Inc., PO Box 5100, Carlsbad, CA 92018-5100.
Tel.: (1) 760 431 7695 or (800) 654 5126; Fax: (1) 760 431 6948 or
(800) 650 5115. www.hayhouse.com

Published and distributed in Australia by:
Hay House Australia Ltd, 18/36 Ralph St, Alexandria NSW 2015.
Tel.: (61) 2 9669 4299; Fax: (61) 2 9669 4144. www.hayhouse.com.au

Published and distributed in the Republic of South Africa by:
Hay House SA (Pty), Ltd, PO Box 990, Witkoppen 2068.
Tel./Fax: (27) 11 467 8904. www.hayhouse.co.za

Published and distributed in India by:
Hay House Publishers India, Muskaan Complex, Plot No.3, B-2, Vasant Kunj,
New Delhi – 110 070. Tel: (91) 11 41761620; Fax: (91) 11 41761630.
www.hayhouse.co.in

Distributed in Canada by:
Raincoast, 9050 Shaughnessy St, Vancouver, BC V6P 6E5.
Tel.: (1) 604 323 7100; Fax: (1) 604 323 2600

A catalogue record for this book is available from the British Library.

Cover Design: Leanne Siu
Interior Design: Leanne Siu/e-Digital Design
Illustrations: Juliet Percival
Translation: Dennis McAllister, Nick Handforth www.citylanguages.de

ISBN 978-1-4019-1583-4

Printed and bound in Great Britain by TJ International, Padstow, Cornwall.

Contents

Barbel Mohr and Cosmic Ordering

☆☆☆☆

Barbel Mohr was a photo journalist, photo editor and graphic designer. Then she also started writing in 1995, at first just as a hobby. Her first book, *The Cosmic Ordering Service*, was a huge success. She has now sold over a million books, and feedback from her readers shows how well her method works. She has been giving lectures and seminars for over 10 years. Her most successful seminar is the classic Life Happiness seminar which, among other things, strengthens the 'connection to above'.

'I discovered wishing and ordering for myself almost 15 years ago, though I hadn't believed in it at all before, and so opened the door to this wonderful world of new possibilities. The experiences of my circle of friends and readers have shown that what is most important when wishing or ordering, as in life in general, is that "working together is better!" Whenever we came together and wished for something as a group, each wishing for themselves or all of us wishing for one thing, the success rate was often even higher.'

To read more by or about Barbel, visit www.baerbel-mohr.de.

Pierre Franckh and Successful Wishing

☆ ☆ ☆ ☆

The author and actor Pierre Franckh specialises in the fields of psychology, relationships and eroticism. The result has been the bestselling books *Rules of Happiness for Love* (*Glücksregeln für die Liebe*), *Loving Lustfully* (*Lustvoll Lieben*) and *Successful Wishing* (*Erfolgreich Wünschen*). He was a master of successful wishing even as a child, wishing himself a film role and then acting opposite the lead in a film about cheeky schoolboys by Ludwig Thoma. During his time at school, he lost his 'wonderful knowledge' and gave way to an enlightened, rational scepticism. He only found the path back again to the skill of wishing through a crisis in his life. Wishing has now been a natural part of his life again for over 30 years. Pierre Franckh shares his knowledge and experiences in an inspiring way through his seminars and lectures. He shows us vividly in *Successful Wishing* that everything in life is made possible through the correct use of wishing. The enthusiastic feedback from his readers confirms how superbly his simple rules for wishing actually work for everyone.

For more information, visit www.Pierre-Franckh.de.

Instructions for
Successful Wishing

☆☆☆☆

From *Successful Wishing* by Pierre Franckh.

1. Begin with the little things …

and let your mind be convinced of the possibilities offered by wishing through your first successes. Nothing is as successful as success itself, as success naturally attracts further success.

2. Always wish for things in the present tense,

never in the future. 'I am rich' and not 'I want to be rich'. Otherwise we achieve the state of wanting something and not being something.

3. Act as if we already have the thing that we wish for.

In this way we are constantly dealing with what is to come in a positive way and can prepare ourselves by looking forward to it. This gives us the correct vibrations. We literally pull the event into our lives. 'Not' and 'nothing' have no place in wishing. Otherwise we pull all the things we want to avoid into our lives because we give them energy through our thoughts. Feeling anxious attracts exactly those events we want to prevent. 'I don't want to get ill,' in terms of wish energy means, 'I want to get ill.' We can't prevent something from happening. We can only ever create something and not 'not create' it. Just the thought of 'not creating' it will make the unwanted thing happen, because we are thinking and worrying about it. So wanting to avoid something doesn't work, but we can let its opposite take place. We just have to deal with its corresponding parallel.

'I am well.' This order is simple and clear. This wish allows us to deal with our health and not with illness.

4. Write the wish down.

When we write it down we give our wish substance. From now on it exists physically. It is our firm will, unshakeable, clear and unambiguous.

It also lets us check when the wish has been fulfilled. What did I really wish for and must I improve my formulating so that I receive the thing that I wish for from the bottom of my heart? Writing wishes down makes it easier to work with them. This diary is perfect for this purpose.

5. Clear, short and precise formulation.

The more precise we are in formulating the wish, the more exactly it will be carried out. The more precise and succinct we are, the more we are forced to discover what lies at the heart of our wish. If you can express it in two sentences, you know yourself much more exactly what you are really wishing for.

6. Giving thanks.

We increase the goodness by thanking, as we start to examine the things in our lives which are going well. We give them attention and recognition. Whatever is given attention is also given energy. Giving thanks allows us to increase all of the good things that already exist in our lives, because we give them even more energy.

Giving thanks brings the wish into the present. This is similar to saying 'amen' at the end of a prayer. In translation, 'amen' means 'certain, true!'; this means it is in the present. The energy from praying and the energy from wishing are very similar. In both cases we cry out to a higher being and ask for a solution. We sign off or close each of these by saying amen or by giving thanks.

Giving thanks sweeps away all doubt and worry. We believe it will happen. We are certain. In daily life you also only give thanks for things that have already been confirmed. 'Thank you for taking care of it for me.' So you only give thanks for things that you are absolutely certain will also be carried out. By giving thanks, we are confirming our order. The wish is signed off, like the signature at the end of a document.

7. Trust instead of doubt.

Doubt is a very clear wish that will be carried out. By doubting, you call back your wishes almost before they have been sent out. Often, at the same time as making the wish, people say or think, 'It's not going to work anyway.' This thought, however, is nothing other than a precise wish, which is, 'It doesn't work.' And what will happen? This wish is sent out and will be delivered as ordered. We are always successful, most often by being the authors of our own failures. Those who don't believe in success cannot be successful. Trust, therefore, in the fact that your wish will be fulfilled.

8. Secrecy.

You can weaken your wish by speaking about it. On the one hand, the energy is dissipated by the constant 'wear and tear'. On the other hand, we quickly attract opponents, people who are jealous and doubt the plan, and give space to their beliefs and convictions.

9. Forgetting.

This has many advantages. First, when we forget about our wish, we also forget to doubt and so don't reverse the entire order process again. Second, we prove how great our trust is, as we are so certain that the thing we wish for will come into our lives that we don't work at it any more. This also allows us to be open to accepting the thing that we are wishing for when it arrives, no matter how unsuitable it may be to our current situation.

10. Being open for coincidences.

You can't plan how your wish will be delivered. Wishes are almost always fulfilled in a way that you would never have believed possible. So you should simply just expect that the wish will be fulfilled. The cosmos finds its own way and there is no way we can know what it will be.

11. Intuition.

As everything is a question of energy, we are sometimes 'only' led very gently to the place where the thing we are wishing for can be found. If you have sent out a wish, the best thing is to keep your ears pricked and to stay alert. This will let you gather all of the information you need. If you want to come into closer contact with your intuition, the only thing you have to do is to follow up on the things that feel right to you.

12.Discovering your big true wishes.

Which wishes suit me? This is the most important question. There is no point in wishing for something that goes against your own nature, even if most of us do this anyway. We often wish for something just because others are wishing for it or already have it. We often run after an ideal that isn't our own at all. Before we wish for something, we have to be clear that it is something that we actually need in our lives. Will it make us feel better, more loveable or more accepted? Every successful wish also changes the circumstances of our lives. This is why we should be absolutely sure that we are also actually ready for this change. So find out what your true yearnings and wishes are, so that they can also make you happy.

Wish, and be ready to let miracles into your life.

How Can I Use the Full Potential of This Diary?

The wonderful thing about this *Wish Book* is that it can teach us to wish in the most perfect way.

1. First we simply write down our wish in our diary.

This will strengthen our wish. The wish leaves our body physically for the first time. It also gains strength just by doing this. Suddenly we are being serious about it. We are leaving the realms of speculation and dreams, which we are still not convinced about. From now on our wish is physical, it is our stated will, unshakeable, clear and resolute.

If we just go about wishing willy-nilly, at some point we will no longer remember all of the things we have wished for, and after a while we will lose our overview. Not only this, but we won't just be wishing for something; instead we will most probably be constantly wishing for something, then wishing for the opposite, wishing anew, and then again for something completely different. We often don't really want what we wish for, but are taken with the idea for a moment and a moment later wish for something very different. The Universe doesn't mind. Whatever is wished for will be delivered, even if we don't have any use for it any more. We suddenly find ourselves buried in a heap of wishes we have sent out and no longer have an overview of our lives. Then all sorts of different and contradictory things start to happen all around us and, in the chaos, we no longer realise that we are the authors of all of these events.

Add to this all of our unconscious wishes that we really don't want to happen. We find ourselves once again exactly back where we no longer want to be: things happen and we don't have a clue who ordered all of them to happen. It is therefore better to realise our first wishes very deliberately and give them a clear direction and importance by writing them down.

2. Then over the following days, we keep an eye out for all of those 'coincidences' that happen around us and note these down in our diary as well.

We just stay alert and write everything down that attracts our attention. Many of these things have nothing to do with our wish. Many, however, do.

If you always just look in the one direction that you expect the delivery to come from, it might be that you miss the delivery completely, because you are waiting for the order to be fulfilled only in the exact way that it is possible for you to imagine, due to our very limited powers of thought. The Universe, however, is much more imaginative. When it happens, we are then happy to see it as a miracle because we are so surprised that there have suddenly been so many 'coincidences' in our lives that have allowed our wish to be fulfilled. In truth it is just our wish becoming reality and this often happens in a way that we had not bargained for.

3. The diary helps us sharpen our intuition.

Our intuition often leads us to where we find the thing we are wishing for 'by coincidence'. This can sometimes be something that someone said that we happened to overhear, but that contained important information for us. It can also be a thought that we then follow up. Or you happen to choose to go somewhere by a different route and 'coincidentally' meet an old friend, who 'happens' to tell you about someone you ought to meet, and 'strangely enough' this person has exactly the thing that you wished for – the new flat, the plunger to unblock your drains – or maybe knows someone who can fix your computer problem.

If you want to get in closer contact with your intuition, you simply have to follow up on anything that feels right to you. No matter how strange, embarrassing or silly it might seem at first glance. Intuition is nothing more than making a spontaneous decision. If something occurs to you that you would like to do, then do it. Don't look for reasons for or against it. Don't weigh up the options – follow the impulse.

With the help of your intuition, your decisions will be more spontaneous and your trust in your own perceptions will grow. Instead of having to meet the challenges of daily life ourselves, we let ourselves drift to the solution we wished for. It is really nothing more than recapturing the fine particles of energy that we sent out initially. In coming back to us, it now leads us to where our wish will be fulfilled. We can see how wonderfully our intuition leads us by the entries we make in our diary.

4. Recognizing our own doubts.

When wishes aren't fulfilled, it is usually because a second wish exists that is stronger than the first. This second wish is then definitely working against the first, more forcefully and with greater determination. This second wish is mostly called 'doubt'.

The consciously formulated wish is often overlaid by unintentional doubts. We can see how successful wishing actually is but how persistently the negative wish, or the obstruction, enters into our lives.

All of the positive thinking, all of the mantras in the world, are no help if we are constantly thinking internally about problems and restrictions. Doubt is an attitude with deep roots, a firmly anchored belief that can make itself come true just as easily as your conscious wish. (For more on this, see the box on the following page.)

5. Checking our wishes.

Have I got what I wished for? There is another advantage to making entries in the diary. It is a fabulous way to track evidence. After a short while we tend to forget exactly what we wished for. We still know the rough meaning of our wish, but the words can often get mixed up in our memories after a while. This isn't surprising, as countless new influences flood over us every single day. We change, our thoughts change and so do our memories, which often reflect an inseparable mixture of fact, thoughts and hopes.

If the wish is delivered and you can check the original order again, you will often be wonderfully surprised. You are amazed when you see how precisely the wish has been fulfilled according to the written order. Now we can start to work on our original wish formulation. What have I received? Is it exactly what I wanted? If yes, hurray! If not, which words do I have to change? Why was it fulfilled differently? Which words didn't fit the wish energy I sent out?

This helps you to formulate your wish better, more precisely and more exactly. What did we actually want?

In this way we can quickly become true experts in wishing.

Working with the 'doubt cross'

Every time we have doubts about our wish, we make a little cross against it in the diary. We will be surprised how many little crosses pile up after a very short time. This is just proof of how strongly we believe in the non-fulfilment of our wishes. But doubt isn't so bad if you don't take it too seriously. If we don't give our doubts any energy, they won't have any effect. The best thing is to accept the doubts, but not to evaluate them. They are there, they bubble to the surface and are noted – they are only doubts after all, which we shouldn't be giving any power or meaning – and are released again and sent on their way without a comment.

Behind each 'doubt cross', add a 'take-no-notice tick'. You will be surprised at how quickly over a year the doubts disappear and are replaced as a deep-rooted basic trust enters your life.

Another method from Barbel
Just imagine that you are crossing out a doubt with each cross you make, and are taking away all its energy and force. All of the crosses in the diary are then all the doubts that you have 'located, holed and finally sunk' as in the game Battleships. The more crosses you have, the more successful you were in 'doubt sinking'.

And now for some tips from Barbel's *The Cosmic Ordering Service*:

The Cosmic Ordering Service

What often puts the brakes on wishes is unconscious thought patterns and doubts. Just try ordering from the cosmos. Our unconscious associates the word 'ordering' with a feeling of certainty that the order will arrive.

You can write your order in the diary and imagine that you are sending a 'fax to the Universe's mail-order warehouse'. You then do exactly what you do with all other mail-order companies: get on with your daily tasks and stop thinking about it.

To strengthen it you can practise your exercises in giving thanks. This leads to an automatic process of release at the level of the unconscious. To do this we concentrate on diverting our attention to 'giving thanks for the little things' instead of 'worrying about when exactly it is going to arrive'.

Act like the ancient Indians

Imagine what it would be like if you already had the thing that you wished for. How would you feel? What would your daily routine be, how would it change? Experience the feeling as intensely as you can of 'what it would be like.' As soon as you can really feel it, give thanks for it. This is a further powerful way of bringing your wish to life.

☆ ☆ ☆ ☆

The Power of Togetherness

☆☆☆☆

The power of praying/wishing for others

Ho'oponopono is a Hawaiian healing technique that has many aspects. One of these states that you can heal everything inside yourself that you don't like on the outside. This is possible because all is one and the world as we experience it is only an illusion. Everything that exists is connected to, and influences, everything else. This doesn't only apply to the subatomic level, but also, according to Hawaiian philosophy, to the energetic and spiritual planes. 'Heal the resonances within yourself and others will cease to experience them on the outside.' This can go so far that people change their behaviour or become healthier because you stop feeling angry with them. Because you heal the resonances within yourself, you heal them in others as well. For more information see my website, www.baerbelmohr.de.

Together for everyone

We can use this knowledge to a) send our own wishes into the Universe and b) make wishes for everyone else and the natural world of the entire planet.

My wish would be that as many of you as possible close your very personal wishes and orders with the following words:

'... and I wish that the wishes of everybody else that is

ordering and wishing along with me today are also fulfilled, to the good of those people and of everybody
involved! I send my thanks, my love and my wishes for
healing for every level of the planet Earth, the natural
world and the entire Universe.'

Even Einstein was of the opinion that the natural world
tended towards harmony. When all people reconnect
with their innermost nature and so find their personal
harmony and fulfilment, and wish exactly the same for
everyone else, we will have achieved world peace! I am
convinced of this.

☆☆☆☆

Your Monthly Date with Yourself

☆☆☆☆

This diary offers you a wealth of information and topics for each month. All you need to do now is to make enough time to work with them …

It's simple: make a date with yourself! Write down a time and date each month for you to see yourself. Whether it's two, three or five hours or even a whole day depends on how it fits into your life. You can manage two hours a month with a bit of organization, even if you have five children.

Maybe you want to start your date with yourself with a little meditation on self-love in front of the mirror. Then you can go through the topics for the month and make notes on where you are at the moment and where you want to get to in your life. Examine your current state honestly and love yourself in spite of it, or because of it.

Imagine the goal you wish for as vividly as if it were already there. How would it feel? How would you feel with it? Write this feeling down in your diary and keep an eye on how it develops.

Close your date with yourself by treating yourself to something. I'm thinking less of shopping or TV here, and more of listening to your favourite music, having a bath etc.

Wish Dates

The wish dates already marked in this diary are particularly favourable for sending off wishes and for ordering! There are astrological and numerological dates chosen, turbo-wish dates that have been selected by a medium, and favourable dates chosen according to the Mayan calendar.

Astrologically chosen wish dates

Among the astrologically chosen dates are the new moon dates. You can wish all day long, but the force is strongest half an hour after the new moon has risen and for the following two hours.

The new moon strengthens all wishes that deal with new beginnings and with growth: more money, health, a new … The full moon is a good time to let go of something. For example, to say goodbye to a bad habit. Then there are also times when aspects of certain topics are astrologically favourable. These are mostly several days in succession and you can see from the list of wish dates which symbols stand for which qualities.

Turbo-wish dates

There are turbo dates specially selected by several mediums with an exact time, which only lasts for a few minutes. This means that everyone making a wish then, makes it at exactly the same time. Who knows whether it is because our mediums are so good, whether faith moves mountains or whether it was due to the synchronised timing or the community of wishers, but in 2007 these dates worked especially well and also led to wonderful meditation experiences and 'delivery success'.

There are also turbo-wish dates with Barbel and Pierre. Three times a year the turbo-wish date symbol appears with two extra little stars next to it. This means that Barbel and Pierre will be wishing and ordering with you at exactly these times, for themselves and for everyone else.

Wish dates according to the Mayan calendar

The Mayan calendar is an ancient calendar which has remained unchanged since Mayan times, unlike our Gregorian calendar, which was last altered in the 16th century. The start of the Mayan year is 26th July and not 1st January. This is explained by the fact that a particular constellation of stars can be seen in the sky every year on this day. It is on this day that our sun is in conjunction with our second nearest star, Alcyone (in the pleiadian system), and with the star Sirius B.

The final day of the Mayan year is 24th July and the following day, 25th July, is the so-called 'green day', the day outside time. This day connects the old year to the new. Johan Koessner (www.maya.at), a famous Mayan calendar expert, writes that we also have a 'personal green day' and that this is the day before our birthday. It is a kind of personal day outside time and therefore also very favourable for wishing and for setting new impulses.

Your Daily Affirmation

You will find a short sentence for each day in the diary. These affirmations have been created in such a way that they fit the special quality of that day. They will help you to work against unwanted things or strengthen the positive in a targeted way. They help us to centre the day and remind us of our true nature. If we consciously think of this sentence repeatedly throughout the day, it helps us to be true to ourselves and listen to our inner voice. This makes everything easier as it means we are going along with the flow of life.

Play with the affirmations, use them as the motto of the day and check in the evening how they have changed your day. You will notice after a very short time how much more consciously you live your life and this in itself has a positive effect on your wishing as it helps you to notice more easily the little signs, the 'coincidences', through which your wish might just be being fulfilled.

At the Beginning of the Month

At the beginning of each month you will find the best wish formulations on a topic by Pierre or a success story from Barbel's readers.

If you experience particularly wonderful things on the communal wishing dates, please contact us at kalendar@baerbelmohr.de or kalendar@pierrefranckh.de. If you are particularly lucky, you might win one of our three Christmas surprise parcels. For those who don't want to be surprised, but would prefer instead to win a free Life Happiness seminar with Barbel for two people or a one-to-one coaching session with Pierre, please let us know. And of course don't forget to include your address!

Stories of successful ordering

These stories are meant to inspire you, so that you come up with lots of wonderful ideas and don't always just order yourself a parking space …

'Use it or lose it,' as it is so neatly put – and this isn't just true for muscles but also for your connection to the Universe!

Hot tip: don't just call the Universe into your thoughts when you have a problem, but also share your happiness with it. 'Hey, Universe, did you see that? – a great fire-work display, a laughing child, a great success – sooo beautiful, and I'm sending some of my joy up to you!' This exercises your connection to above as well!

☆ ☆ ☆ ☆

Formulating wishes

The book *Successful Wishing* has positively changed the lives of countless people. However, I am still asked in my lectures if there is a pre-formulated guide for various wishes, a so-called template for successful wishing.

Although each wish is truly individual, there is what you might call a general 'template' that works on a general level. The following wish formulations will lead you to a precisely defined energy stream, so that everything inside you can open itself up to whatever you would like to invite into your life.

Simply choose a topic that you find interesting and take the wish formulation that feels best for you and where you feel the lowest level of opposition. This is a good key for unlocking the door to the energy of your wish.

Whenever you notice after sending out a wish that doubts are ruling your thoughts once again, just turn to your wish formulation and repeat it until you feel the power and peace that it sends out once again.

☆ ☆ ☆ ☆

Key to Symbols

All wish dates are either astrological, numerological, selected by a medium or a combination of all three.

 Job: You can wish for the perfect job, or a stress-free job and good communication on the days when you see this computer.

 Forgiveness: Forgiving yourself and others is a prerequisite for being able to love with your whole heart.

 Changing old patterns: Wish for the necessary impulse, to escape from the prison of unwanted but deep-rooted patterns and programmes.

 Spiritual encounters: Spirituality, erotic attraction and the pure love of life are part of this.

 Feeling comfortable at home: A new home, peace with the neighbours, a new sofa and generally everything to do with living.

 Health: Order yourself help for health on all levels, to stay healthy or to become healthy.

 Holidays: Today is the day for all wishes connected to your dream holiday.

 Children: A harmonious family life is an important wish to make. Ideas and solutions for problems at school can also be ordered here.

The new moon: The new moon strengthens all wishes which deal with a new beginning or with growth (for more on this see page 24) and the wish force is strongest half an hour after the new moon has risen and for the following two hours!

Full moon: The full moon is a good time to let go of something or to free yourself from bad habits. Above all, it is the ideal day for inner peace and reflection. Are my wishes truly heartfelt? Which signs and coincidences have already shown themselves? In which situations have I listened to my inner voice and when haven't I?

Money: You can order money, or better yet, the thing that you want the money for. For example, order a house rather than the money to buy a house. This leaves more options open for the Universe to deliver.

Relationships: The days with the hearts are particularly suited to your wishes for harmony in your existing relationship or for a new partner if you are single.

Turbo-wish dates: The turbo dates selected by the mediums are particularly powerful as they only last for a few minutes and as everyone who is taking part is wishing at exactly the same moment, which amplifies the power.

Turbo-wish date with Barbel and Pierre: We will be wishing and ordering at this exact time on three dates in the year for ourselves and for the fulfilment of the wishes of everyone taking part at that moment.

Weekday motto to strengthen your personality and intuition for better wish fulfilment

Monday: This is the day for a new beginning. Whatever you want to change or to do differently, Monday is always a good time to start. Monday is also a good day for thinking about things in a new way.

Tuesday: This day is totally dedicated to serving the Universe. Today I will pay close attention to impulses and to 'signs from above'.

Wednesday: Today I will have complete calm at my centre, no matter what happens.

Thursday: Today I will stand up for myself; if necessary by using a 'cleansing thunderstorm'.

Friday: Today I am free of all negative thoughts. On this day I will only pay attention to positive things.

Saturday: The name Saturday comes from the Hebrew *Schabbat* and the Latin *Sabbata*. This is a holiday for some religious groups, and we accept this meaning and use Saturday to relax and to enter stillness and peace, even if this is only for half an hour. Stillness gives your soul the space to show you your calling and your heart-felt wishes more clearly.

Sunday: The day of the Sun and of yang energy. Exercise in the fresh air is good on this day.

Treat This Diary as a
Little Exercise Book

☆☆☆☆

This is why the daily entries are so important. We can follow our wishes from their creation, through their development, through the apparent 'coincidences' connected to them, our changing attitudes to our wishes and of course the number of doubt crosses. This is how we come to understand what we really believe about ourselves. Only once we discover what we really want can we begin to give direction to working with our wishes.

And we naturally have more than one wish at the same time. Therefore it is good to work with a kind of shorthand. We have big wishes and little wishes. Some are delivered straight away, others take longer to process and, of course, sometimes only our doubts are delivered.

Keep the book for several years so that you can check how successful you have become and how expertly you now go about practising your daily wishing.

Weekly Diary
2008

☆☆☆

Happiness

☆☆☆☆

Take one or more of these affirmations and use them to strengthen your wishes.

True happiness always comes from inside.

Happiness is a question of attitude.

I'm deciding now to be happy.

Everything that I experience is an expression of purest love.

I can take control of my own life.

Only my imagination can allow something to happen or prevent it from happening.

My expectations are often disappointed if I expect to be disappointed.

The life I lead is always just a reflection of my inner reality.

I can change my life every day.

Today is a good day.

January 2008 week 1

31 monday

22.12-22.15

I look ahead courageously

1 tuesday

0.15-0.19

I search for beauty

2 wednesday

I handle stress creatively and playfully

3 thursday

I wish for a nice girl to
chat me up and ask me out.

I make sure to recognize connections

friday **4**

I wished for a
new car mirror.
Received random txt message from
unknown girl.

I am at peace with myself and with the world

saturday **5**

I honour Mother Earth and her gifts

sunday **6**

Put a wish in to sell
My Towbar + HP Ipaq.

Other people are a mirror for me

wish notes for the week

January 2008

7 monday

I begin something new

8 tuesday

11.34

HP Ipaq Sold
on Ebay but to dodgy
Seller,

I reorganize my life

9 wednesday

I recognize my innermost wish

10 thursday

Each day is a day of transformation

friday **11**

I am proud of myself

saturday **12**

I spend this day surrounded by nature

sunday **13**

I remain flexible inside

wish notes for the week

January 2008 week 3

14 monday

I let go of something that does not fit into my life

15 tuesday

I congratulate myself on my achievements

16 wednesday

I fulfil a heartfelt wish

17 thursday

16.10-16.20

I free myself of a burden

friday **18**

I integrate work and pleasure in my life

saturday **19**

I give structure to my visions

sunday **20**

I am childlike and naive

wish notes for the week

January 2008 week 4

21 monday

I accept responsibility

22 tuesday

13.38

My life is full of positive surprises

23 wednesday

I show character and my sense of honour

24 thursday

I strive for my ideal

friday **25**

I recognize the work of providence

saturday **26**

My sensuality is an expression of my love of life

sunday **27**

I take a step back and make a new plan

wish notes for the week

January 2008 week 5

28 monday

I applaud myself for my achievements

29 tuesday

I take care of the people around me

30 wednesday

I am proud of my sense of responsibility

31 thursday

I am calm and composed

friday **1**

This day, light as a feather, I give myself as a gift

saturday **2**

I gather strength from harmony

sunday **3**

I value the people around me

wish notes for the week

Armchair Delivery

I would never for the life of me have believed that a wish could be fulfilled in the following way. My parents had had the same armchairs for over 30 years and, as you can guess, they weren't in very good condition. One day, my mother stood in front of them and said, 'You know, it's really about time we got some new ones.' As my father is generally against change, he tried to convince us that the old ones were still good enough after all. My mother sighed but sent off an unconscious wish with her thoughts, 'But I want to have new ones, and that's final!' A week later she was taking the dogs for a walk when she noticed something strange on the other side of the hill. It looked a little bit like armchairs. She walked over and saw that she was right. Someone had unceremoniously dumped their armchairs in the middle of the countryside. They weren't new but were in much better condition than her old ones at home. Excited and still finding it hard to believe her luck, she hurried to get her car and loaded the armchairs into it. The cosmos is amazing!

From Susanne in Vienna.

Progress

☆☆☆☆

Compare your entries from last month with the same month last year. If you are working with this calendar for the first time, compare each finished month with the month before.

- Which wishes have already been fulfilled and how were they fulfilled?

- Are your unfulfilled wishes still up-to-date or have some of your goals and wishes changed?

- Compare your entries: which ones worked particularly well in your daily life, where can you make improvements?

- Which of your entries repeat themselves?

- How have your doubt crosses developed?

- What effects do you feel when working with the daily affirmations?

February 2008 week 6

4 monday

I sense and feel things particularly intensely

5 tuesday

I am creating more space for myself

6 wednesday

I listen to my inner child today

7 thursday

3.41

I can overcome this internal boundary

friday **8**

New ideas are breaking into my life

saturday **9**

I believe in myself

sunday **10**

I recognize my own nature

wish notes for the week

February 2008 week 7

11 monday

I am fulfilling a heartfelt wish

12 tuesday

I am listening to the voice inside me

13 wednesday

The beauty of nature fills me with joy

14 thursday

I am great the way I am

friday **15**

My problems help me to grow

saturday **16**

I am bravely doing the thing that I am afraid of

sunday **17**

16.10-16.20

I am fighting for my ideals

wish notes for the week

February 2008 week 8

18 monday

My feelings are my true potential

19 tuesday

I am discovering my positive qualities

20 wednesday

I recognize my true value

21 thursday

3.31

I am surrounded by beauty

friday **22**

I am creating a new, comprehensive image of myself

saturday **23**

I am completely changing something in my life

sunday **24**

The old makes way for the new

wish notes for the week

February 2008 week 9

25 **monday**

I am following a greater vision

26 **tuesday**

My creativity is unfolding

27 **wednesday**

Every mistake has a deeper reason

28 **thursday**

I am resolute in renewing myself

friday **29**

I am as innocent and carefree as a child

saturday **1**

This is a day to sense and to experience

sunday **2**

I am following my impulses

wish notes for the week

Love and Partnerships

☆ ☆ ☆ ☆

Take one or more of these affirmations and use them to strengthen your wishes.

I see with the eyes of love.

Everything that I encounter is the best for my life.

I am creating the life I really want to lead, here and now.

I am unique and beautiful and come closer to loving myself every day.

I am open and ready to let love appear in my life.

I allow the love in my heart to radiate outwards.

I am open and ready to love myself and let in the love of another person.

Until you are ready inside, all searching is senseless.

The best partner is always the one who truly suits us – and that is always the one who sees the world with the same eyes.

Progress

☆☆☆☆

Compare your entries from last month with the same month last year. If you are working with this calendar for the first time, compare each finished month with the month before.

- Which wishes have already been fulfilled and how were they fulfilled?

- Are your unfulfilled wishes still up-to-date or have some of your goals and wishes changed?

- Compare your entries: which ones worked particularly well in your daily life, where can you make improvements?

- Which of your entries repeat themselves?

- How have your doubt crosses developed?

- What effects do you feel when working with the daily affirmations?

March 2008 week 10

3 monday

I find a new solution deep inside me

4 tuesday

I listen to my inner voice

5 wednesday

I nurture my tender feelings

6 thursday

I keep discovering wonderful new things

friday **7**

17.10

My belief gives me strength

saturday **8**

I am a spiritual being

sunday **9**

I always find the best solution

wish notes for the week

March 2008 week 11

10 monday

I take up a challenge

11 tuesday

I find the easiest way

12 wednesday

I overcome my inner inhibitions

13 thursday

I listen to providence

friday **14**

My sensitivity is a valuable gift

saturday **15**

I give myself recognition

sunday **16**

I trust and believe in myself

wish notes for the week

March 2008 week 12

17 monday

6.10-6.20

I make a great effort to find clarity today

18 tuesday

I am curious and open to everything I encounter

19 wednesday

Persistence leads to the goal

20 thursday

I trust my intuition

friday **21**

18.41

Love will find a way

saturday **22**

I approach things and address them directly

sunday **23**

I see everything in a new light

wish notes for the week

24 monday

Simple solutions are the best

25 tuesday

I implement my ideas in a dynamic way

26 wednesday

I am true to myself

27 thursday

I am making more room for my feminine side

friday **28**

I am open to new things in my life

saturday **29**

I examine my life very closely today

sunday **30**

I give my visions new expression

wish notes for the week

Ordering Appointments to Change – But in a Way that Suits Everyone!

Gabriele and Thorsten gave a Halloween party at their house in 2006. A good friend of Gabriele's called her two weeks before the party to say that she was very sorry but wouldn't be able to come. She had her regular group meeting on exactly that evening, and had already missed one meeting that month and didn't want to miss another. She was sad, though, because she would really have preferred to come to the party. 'Then let's just order the cosmos to cancel the meeting on that day, in a way that suits everyone, and then you can come,' said Gabriele happily.

The week before the party, the friend in question went to her evening meeting. Towards the end of the lesson, the teacher announced that, unfortunately, the lesson next week was cancelled! The friend was astounded and rang Gabrielle and Thorsten immediately afterwards. When Thorsten answered, she shouted excitedly into the phone; 'Your wife is a witch, did you know that...?'

'If she is, then she's only a white witch,' thought Thorsten and was very happy that the friend could come to the party after all.

Progress

☆☆☆☆

Compare your entries from last month with the same month last year. If you are working with this calendar for the first time, compare each finished month with the month before.

- Which wishes have already been fulfilled and how were they fulfilled?

- Are your unfulfilled wishes still up-to-date or have some of your goals and wishes changed?

- Compare your entries: which ones worked particularly well in your daily life, where can you make improvements?

- Which of your entries repeat themselves?

- How have your doubt crosses developed?

- What effects do you feel when working with the daily affirmations?

31 monday

I love and accept myself

1 tuesday

I am bringing an issue to a satisfactory conclusion

2 wednesday

I stand behind my ideals

3 thursday

My inner fire gives me strength

friday **4**

I am listening to my gut feelings

saturday **5**

I am thorough in following things through

sunday **6**

4.53

Power and strength are with me today

wish notes for the week

7 monday

I am transforming something old into something new

8 tuesday

I always find a way

9 wednesday

Every challenge makes me braver

10 thursday

I am proud of my knowledge

friday **11**

I am happy to compete

saturday **12**

My resolve is strong

sunday **13**

A good day to put big plans into practice

wish notes for the week

April 2008 week 16

14 monday

I stick to the tried and tested

15 tuesday

I reinvent myself

16 wednesday

I discover the beauty in others

17 thursday

16.10-16.20

I am serious and thorough

friday **18**

I am confident in myself

saturday **19**

I am beautiful

11.27

sunday **20**

Everything is on the right track

wish notes for the week

April 2008 week 17

21 monday

I am sometimes an egotist, in a positive way

22 tuesday

I give voice to my feelings

23 wednesday

I listen to myself

24 thursday

I look back at my successes

friday **25**

Only the heart sees clearly

saturday **26**

Today I am giving control to my masculine side

sunday **27**

I am enough for myself

wish notes for the week

Creating
☆☆☆☆

Take one or more of these affirmations and use them to strengthen your wishes.

If I don't believe in success, I can't be successful.

Nothing and nobody controls my life; only I do.

Everything is available in abundance, but it is only distributed on request.

Positive thoughts reward us. With negative thoughts, we only punish ourselves.

There are no boundaries. The only boundaries that exist are in my mind.

Everything is energy. The power of thought is pure energy.

Possessions are there for me, I am not there for my possessions.

I am ready, here and now, to let miracles enter my life.

Progress

☆☆☆☆

Compare your entries from last month with the same month last year. If you are working with this calendar for the first time, compare each finished month with the month before.

- Which wishes have already been fulfilled and how were they fulfilled?

- Are your unfulfilled wishes still up-to-date or have some of your goals and wishes changed?

- Compare your entries: which ones worked particularly well in your daily life, where can you make improvements?

- Which of your entries repeat themselves?

- How have your doubt crosses developed?

- What effects do you feel when working with the daily affirmations?

April/May 2008 week 18

28 monday

I believe in myself

29 tuesday

I speak positively about myself and others

30 wednesday

I am happy to be busy

1 thursday

My body feels healthy and happy

friday **2**

I love life

saturday **3**

I am enjoying myself and relaxing

sunday **4**

I am doing everything completely differently for a change

wish notes for the week

May 2008 week 19

5 monday

13.18

My life is full of healing

6 tuesday

I love living life to the full

7 wednesday

I am bubbling over with happiness and enthusiasm

8 thursday

I am giving my body a day of wellness

friday **9**

I look after and take special care of myself today

saturday **10**

I am going for a walk by myself

sunday **11**

I am preparing a little treat for myself today

wish notes for the week

May 2008 week 20

12 monday

My inner child is in control today

13 tuesday

I look at what I have achieved with pride

14 wednesday

I have a really lazy day for once

15 thursday

I discover a new form of pleasure

friday **16**

I find a way to myself

saturday **17**

16.10-16.20

I am calm and at peace

sunday **18**

I breathe in the power of life with a purpose

wish notes for the week

May 2008 week 21

19 monday

I love my body

20 tuesday

 3.09

I am proud of myself

21 wednesday

I give myself a gift

22 thursday

I rearrange my room

friday **2**3

I trust in the flow of life

saturday **24**

I am natural and clear

sunday **25**

I am thankful

wish notes for the week

May 2008 week 22

26 monday

I take up a challenge

27 tuesday

I will do something sporty today

28 wednesday

I dedicate this day to healing myself

29 thursday

Today I am full of energy and strength

friday **30**

I am curious about this change

saturday **31**

I enjoy new things

sunday **1**

I am creative today

wish notes for the week

A Luxury Kitchen at a Bargain-Basement Price

Manuela and Volker had ordered themselves a beautiful house to rent and this had been delivered perfectly. There was only one thing they hadn't thought of: the kitchen. They hadn't ordered one with the house and there wasn't a fitted kitchen included as it was a brand-new house and, as they were the first to move in, they had to bring one with them.

'Well, if we managed to order our house so precisely, then we can also order the kitchen,' thought Manuela, and started to write a long list of all the things she wanted in the new kitchen.

And how much would it cost? That's where it got difficult. They couldn't afford more than 3500 euros. Their landlord had given them the address of a reliable acquaintance who ran a kitchen store in town. They went to see him straightaway, but were shocked to find that the cheapest kitchen there cost 18,500 euros. When the store owner asked them what they were looking for exactly, they told him, and that, at the moment, they only had 3,500 euros to spare. This was at 2 p.m. The three of them got talking and got on really well together. By 2 a.m. they were still sitting there chatting. By this time, the owner of the store had dug out all of the individual items on Manuela's kitchen wish list from three different display kitchens, and offered them the whole lot, including fitting, for exactly 3500 euros. The two could hardly believe their luck.

Progress

Compare your entries from last month with the same month last year. If you are working with this calendar for the first time, compare each finished month with the month before.

- Which wishes have already been fulfilled and how were they fulfilled?

- Are your unfulfilled wishes still up-to-date or have some of your goals and wishes changed?

- Compare your entries: which ones worked particularly well in your daily life, where can you make improvements?

- Which of your entries repeat themselves?

- How have your doubt crosses developed?

- What effects do you feel when working with the daily affirmations?

June 2008 week 23

2 monday

I am creative and express myself well

3 tuesday

20.22

I give voice to my feelings

4 wednesday

My friends are there for me

5 thursday

I have as much curiosity as a child

friday **6**

I find new and interesting paths

saturday **7**

I thank my parents for everything

sunday **8**

I give myself more space

wish notes for the week

9 monday

I discover my own beauty

10 tuesday

I take strength from my roots

11 wednesday

I am happy and healthy

12 thursday

Everything flows lightly and playfully

friday **13**

I am brave and strong

saturday **14**

I have many wonderful skills

sunday **15**

Every new thing enriches me

wish notes for the week

June 2008 week 25

16 monday

I learn from my experiences

17 tuesday

16.10-16.20

I find new interests

18 wednesday

18.30

I forgive myself and others

19 thursday

I react prudently and calmly

friday **20**

I live in perfect harmony

saturday **21**

I follow my dream

sunday **22**

There is power in calmness

wish notes for the week

June 2008 week 26

23 monday

Every new experience enriches me

24 tuesday

I follow my own feelings

25 wednesday

I am sensitive to the feelings of others today

26 thursday

There is a solution to every problem

friday **27**

My heart speaks for me today

saturday **28**

I am full of new inspiration

sunday **29**

I am cheerful and relaxed

wish notes for the week

Successful Wishing

☆☆☆☆

Take one or more of these affirmations and use them to strengthen your wishes.

Reality is created deep within me and only then appears around me.

Energy always follows attention.

What I believe in will come true.

If I don't believe in something, it can't take place in my life.

Every wish already contains the seed of its own fulfilment.

I am open to life and for joy.

Working with the cosmos is far easier than carving out a path alone.

Wishes will be fulfilled exactly as they are ordered.

Progress

Compare your entries from last month with the same month last year. If you are working with this calendar for the first time, compare each finished month with the month before.

- Which wishes have already been fulfilled and how were they fulfilled?

- Are your unfulfilled wishes still up-to-date or have some of your goals and wishes changed?

- Compare your entries: which ones worked particularly well in your daily life, where can you make improvements?

- Which of your entries repeat themselves?

- How have your doubt crosses developed?

- What effects do you feel when working with the daily affirmations?

June/July 2008 week 27

---

30 monday

The only boundaries that exist are in my mind

---

1 tuesday

I am sensitive and open

---

2 wednesday

I look after and take care of myself

---

3 thursday

3.19

I thank my family today

friday **4**

My friends give me strength

saturday **5**

I trust in my inner leadership

sunday **6**

I will get to the bottom of this temptation

wish notes for the week

July 2008 week 28

7 monday

I find myself through peace

8 tuesday

I trust my feelings

9 wednesday

I am rediscovering the world

10 thursday

Every coincidence has a deeper meaning

friday **11**

I breathe love in and breathe love out

saturday **12**

I bring light into my life

sunday **13**

I free myself from old chains

wish notes for the week

July 2008 week 29

14 monday

I express my feelings lovingly

15 tuesday

I love myself

16 wednesday

I am wholly here for myself today

17 thursday

6.10-6.20

I open my heart

friday **18**

8.56

I pay attention to the feelings of others

saturday **19**

I recognize my strengths

sunday **20**

I enjoy life

wish notes for the week

21 monday

I forgive with all my heart

22 tuesday

I am particularly attentive today

23 wednesday

I turn a weakness into a strength

24 thursday

Those who are last will come first

friday **25**

I am the light
'Green day' according to the Mayan Calendar

saturday **26**

I am great the way I am

sunday **27**

I feel the power within me

wish notes for the week

July 2008 week 31

28 monday

My intuition shows me the way

29 tuesday

I am beautiful

30 wednesday

I treat myself with love

31 thursday

I bathe in the rays of love

friday **1**

11.15

I thank everyone who supports me on my path

saturday **2**

My life is full of little gifts

sunday **3**

I trust in my strength

wish notes for the week

Feeling Your Way Towards the Big Partnership Order

Nina went on a camping holiday to Italy with her two children. She was a single mother and didn't really believe that you could simply order a new partner through the cosmos. But, she thought, she could at least try it for the holiday, and so she made the following order, 'Dear cosmos, I am ordering a nice single father with children the same age as mine. His tent should be near ours, and I wish that we have a wonderful time together on holiday.' Her little eight-year-old daughter heard her ordering and shouted to her, 'And Mum, I order that we get a space for the tent right on the beach!'

This was pretty unlikely to happen as it was high season, but amazingly they actually got the space they wanted on the beach, as ordered. Just two days later a new neighbour moved onto the camping site diagonally opposite them. He was single, with two children around the same age as Nina's! They ended up having a very pleasant holiday together.

However, the two of them lived over 1000 kilometres apart and it remained just a good holiday friendship, as ordered. Now Nina started wondering if she should take the plunge and ask for a permanent partner with her next big order. She decided to try it and this order was then also delivered six months later!

Progress

☆☆☆☆

Compare your entries from last month with the same month last year. If you are working with this calendar for the first time, compare each finished month with the month before.

- Which wishes have already been fulfilled and how were they fulfilled?

- Are your unfulfilled wishes still up-to-date or have some of your goals and wishes changed?

- Compare your entries: which ones worked particularly well in your daily life, where can you make improvements?

- Which of your entries repeat themselves?

- How have your doubt crosses developed?

- What effects do you feel when working with the daily affirmations?

August 2008 week 32

4 monday

I am pleased by little things

5 tuesday

I continually rediscover myself

6 wednesday

I feel at home with myself

7 thursday

Change enriches my life

friday **8**

I let go of something

saturday **9**

I enjoy my life

sunday **10**

I am full of childish impatience

wish notes for the week

August 2008 week 33

11 monday

I open myself to inspiration

12 tuesday

Luck is on my side

13 wednesday

Life fills me with pleasure

14 thursday

I enjoy my responsibility

friday **15**

I follow my inner child

saturday **16**

22.15

I stay true to myself

sunday **17**

16.10-16.20

I am going to write down my heartfelt wishes now

wish notes for the week

August 2008 week 34

18 monday

I pass my joy on to others

19 tuesday

My life is a cornucopia

20 wednesday

I accept my darker sides

21 thursday

Everything is fine as it is

friday **22**

I find the best way to solve the issue

saturday **23**

Everything is going the right way

sunday **24**

I see the beauty in each moment

wish notes for the week

25 monday

I love myself the way I am

26 tuesday

I am overflowing with happiness

27 wednesday

I believe in myself

28 thursday

Everything is complete

friday **29**

I bring more colour into my life

saturday **30**

20.59

I am full of energy and desire for action

sunday **31**

I trust life

wish notes for the week

Letting Go

Take one or more of these affirmations and use them to strengthen your wishes.

I let go of all of my old patterns and limitations.

If I don't work on myself, others will work on me.

If I want to change the situation around me, I have to change myself.

Wherever we go, we always take ourselves along.

When nothing else works, wishing always does.

I am completely open to how the wish fulfils itself in my life.

Searching hinders acceptance.

As long as we are searching, we are bound to a very specific object or goal.

Every moment of my life is new and wonderful.

Progress

☆☆☆☆

Compare your entries from last month with the same month last year. If you are working with this calendar for the first time, compare each finished month with the month before.

- Which wishes have already been fulfilled and how were they fulfilled?

- Are your unfulfilled wishes still up-to-date or have some of your goals and wishes changed?

- Compare your entries: which ones worked particularly well in your daily life, where can you make improvements?

- Which of your entries repeat themselves?

- How have your doubt crosses developed?

- What effects do you feel when working with the daily affirmations?

September 2008 week 36

1 monday

I am complete and good

2 tuesday

My life is filled with abundance

3 wednesday

I achieve a lot in my life

4 thursday

I share my feelings with others

friday **5**

I believe in myself

saturday **6**

I trust in the rhythm of life

sunday **7**

I dedicate this day to being thankful

wish notes for the week

8 monday

I follow my intuition

9 tuesday

Treating others in a friendly and caring way is good for me

10 wednesday

I reach my goals step by step

11 thursday

I discover a theme to my life

friday **12**

Today, I am thankful for the money I have

saturday **13**

I look forward with great confidence

sunday **14**

I thank my inner leadership

wish notes for the week

September 2008 week 38

---

15 monday

10.09

I am proud of myself

---

16 tuesday

When I trust in the power of my soul, I am healed

---

17 wednesday

16.10-16.20

I believe in the way I am

---

18 thursday

I thank my body

friday **19**

I see everything with new eyes

saturday **20**

My inner peace radiates outwards

sunday **21**

I go my own way

wish notes for the week

September 2008 week 39

22 monday

I rest within myself

23 tuesday

Every experience has a positive side

24 wednesday

I thank my inner child

25 thursday

I act on the feelings within me

friday **26**

I thank my family

saturday **27**

There is no goodness, unless you create it

sunday **28**

I feel completely happy and relaxed

wish notes for the week

The Cosmic Alarm Clock

☆☆☆☆

The desk in my office at home looked suspiciously chaotic and I had a bad feeling about it. Some of the piles somewhere probably contained unpaid bills and things that needed to be dealt with urgently. But after taking care of things at home and the three kids, I only manage to deal with the top layer of the piles during the day, and in the evenings I am just too tired. What should I do? I had often promised myself that I would get up at 4 a.m. once every two weeks to deal with the deeper layers, but even when I set my alarm clock for 4 a.m. I was always far too tired to actually get up.

Finally I made a cosmic order to be awake and well rested the next morning at 4 a.m. I had set the alarm clock again, but my husband had turned it off, because he thought that the kids had been playing around with it.

In spite of this, I woke up at 4 a.m. and was more awake and rested than I had ever been at that time. The only problem was that my husband had gone to bed late and had slept on the sofa-bed in the office, so as not to disturb me. Now, of course, I didn't want to disturb him either. But hey presto, the cosmos had thought of everything; just three minutes later, he got up to go to the bathroom and when he came out, it was easy to redirect him into the bedroom so that I could go into the office and get to work!

From Sandra.

Progress

☆☆☆☆

Compare your entries from last month with the same month last year. If you are working with this calendar for the first time, compare each finished month with the month before.

- Which wishes have already been fulfilled and how were they fulfilled?

- Are your unfulfilled wishes still up-to-date or have some of your goals and wishes changed?

- Compare your entries: which ones worked particularly well in your daily life, where can you make improvements?

- Which of your entries repeat themselves?

- How have your doubt crosses developed?

- What effects do you feel when working with the daily affirmations?

29 monday

9.15

I persist in following my goals

30 tuesday

I can find a way to my own truth

1 wednesday

My inner life is reflected in the world around me

2 thursday

I love my neighbour as myself

friday **3**

I am open to new ideas

saturday **4**

I am true to myself even in conflict situations

sunday **5**

The more I give, the more I get back

wish notes for the week

October 2008 week 41

6 monday

My life is becoming wonderful

7 tuesday

I reap what I sow

8 wednesday

I live freely and happily

9 thursday

I am the loving partner that I would wish for myself

friday **10**

I reflect myself in my relationships

saturday **11**

I recognize the strength of my family

sunday **12**

I am full of the desire for action

wish notes for the week

October 2008 week 42

13 monday

I smile at everyone today

14 tuesday

20.59

I don't have to do everything by myself

15 wednesday

I am actively reaching out to the person opposite me

16 thursday

Everything comes in its own time

friday **17**

6.10-6.20

I stand up for my friends

saturday **18**

If this day were my last, what would I still like to do?

sunday **19**

I respect the feelings of others

wish notes for the week

20 monday

I search for deeper insights

21 tuesday

I show myself

22 wednesday

My own clarity helps me to grow

23 thursday

I strive for harmony

friday **24**

I draw strength from nature

saturday **25**

I am surrounded by beauty and abundance

sunday **26**

I say yes to a harmonious relationship

wish notes for the week

October 2008 week 44

27 monday

I recognize myself in my projections

28 tuesday

 23.13

I feel and sense myself

29 wednesday

I ensure harmony at work

30 thursday

I am allowed to enjoy life

friday **31**

I am glad I exist

saturday **1**

Possessions are restricting

sunday **2**

I shed my old skin

wish notes for the week

Trust

☆☆☆☆

Take one or more of these affirmations and use them to strengthen your wishes.

I will be given everything I need at the time I need it.

I can only be given things if I am also prepared to accept them.

I trust in the flow of life.

Being prepared means allowing miracles to enter my life.

When I experience the feeling of wealth deep within me, then I will also experience wealth around me.

My thoughts attract everything that is similar to them.

We already have the things we wish for.

Everything that happens is for my best.

Trusting myself means believing in myself.

Progress

☆ ☆ ☆ ☆

Compare your entries from last month with the same month last year. If you are working with this calendar for the first time, compare each finished month with the month before.

- Which wishes have already been fulfilled and how were they fulfilled?

- Are your unfulfilled wishes still up-to-date or have some of your goals and wishes changed?

- Compare your entries: which ones worked particularly well in your daily life, where can you make improvements?

- Which of your entries repeat themselves?

- How have your doubt crosses developed?

- What effects do you feel when working with the daily affirmations?

3 monday

My body is a gift from the Almighty

4 tuesday

I support myself through love

5 wednesday

I let go of old thought patterns

6 thursday

I enjoy being alone

friday **7**

I dedicate this day to myself

saturday **8**

I look at the conflicts within me and let them go

sunday **9**

Dreams are there to be realised

wish notes for the week

November 2008 week 46

10 monday

I breathe fulfilment in and out

11 tuesday

I love all aspects of my personality

12 wednesday

—

I am ready for change

13 thursday

6.16

I create space for new things in my life

friday **14**

Old thought patterns only work as long as I hold onto them

saturday **15**

I embrace my darker sides

sunday **16**

Love always finds a way

wish notes for the week

November 2008

17 monday

16.10-16.20

I learn something new today

18 tuesday

I pass on my wisdom

19 wednesday

I enchant the world around me

20 thursday

I let go of something I fear

friday **21**

I bravely cross an inner boundary

saturday **22**

I do many things differently today

sunday **23**

I am curious about happiness

wish notes for the week

November 2008 week 48

24 monday

I always look for new things

25 tuesday

This day is turning into a day just for me

26 wednesday

I follow my gut feelings

27 thursday

16.55

I trust my feelings

friday **28**

The more I let go, the freer I become

saturday **29**

I let go of every control

sunday **30**

I can use the power of thought

wish notes for the week

Ordering Tickets and Buying a Piano

Marlena heard about a wonderful concert two days before it was going to take place. Unfortunately it had been sold out for weeks. The next day she was speaking to two friends of hers who also said that they really wanted to go to the concert too. What could they do? Cosmic ordering, of course! Marlena had a few chores to finish around the house before she finally picked up the phone and called the ticket office to tell them that she was looking for three tickets. They told her that she was extremely lucky and that, only two minutes ago, three tickets had been returned!

Marlena is a frequent cosmic orderer. Just before Christmas, she realized that she had to sell her piano. First because it was hardly ever played, and second because her guests at Christmas would have no room at the table in her little flat – unless the piano went.

Unfortunately, she had missed the final deadline for placing an ad, so she had to make another order. More in desperation than in hope, she asked her daughter's art tutor if she by any chance needed a piano. She was very surprised when she actually said yes, and asked if she could pick it up straightaway. Marlena was even happy about the price – a year of free art classes for her daughter!

Progress

☆☆☆☆

Compare your entries from last month with the same month last year. If you are working with this calendar for the first time, compare each finished month with the month before.

- Which wishes have already been fulfilled and how were they fulfilled?

- Are your unfulfilled wishes still up-to-date or have some of your goals and wishes changed?

- Compare your entries: which ones worked particularly well in your daily life, where can you make improvements?

- Which of your entries repeat themselves?

- How have your doubt crosses developed?

- What effects do you feel when working with the daily affirmations?

December 2008 week 49

1 monday

I feel like a queen or king

2 tuesday

I create my own world

3 wednesday

I am in contact with my angel

4 thursday

I love and forgive

friday **5**

I will only say positive things about people today

saturday **6**

Life makes me so happy

sunday **7**

I live straight from the heart

wish notes for the week

December 2008 week 50

8 monday

I experience an ideal day today

9 tuesday

My life is a cornucopia

10 wednesday

I can also reach my goals in a playful way

11 thursday

I keep finding new sides to myself

friday **12**

16.38

I can achieve anything

saturday **13**

I share my inner wealth with others

sunday **14**

Every day turns out best for me

wish notes for the week

December 2008 week 51

15 monday

I accept myself lovingly

16 tuesday

My ideals are becoming clear

17 wednesday

16.10-16.20

Every new insight makes me glad

18 thursday

I see the special side of every person

friday **19**

I look back at my life with grace

saturday **20**

I show myself as I actually am

sunday **21**

I don't have to do everything perfectly

wish notes for the week

22 monday

I feel loved by everyone today

23 tuesday

True magnanimity is shown in resolving a dispute

24 wednesday

The best solution is when everyone is a winner

25 thursday

I dedicate this day to looking back over the year

friday **26**

I value open communication

saturday **27**

12.22

I am special

sunday **28**

My home is an expression of the satisfaction within me

wish notes for the week

29 monday

I sense and discover my surroundings

30 tuesday

I am in perfect harmony with myself and all around me

31 wednesday

I look back on a year full of positive experiences

1 thursday

I plan my future with complete confidence

friday **2**

I look forward to the year with great expectations

saturday **3**

Every day is a heavenly gift

sunday **4**

I am full of thanks and happiness

wish notes for the week

Personal Details

☆☆☆☆

Name

Address

Telephone No.

Mobile No.

Email

My List of Wishes

☆☆☆☆

28/3/08

1) I wish for a girlfriend ✓

2) I want Bully to fully ⚹ download and Play. ↓

3) I want to sell my laptop ⚹ for at least £250. ⁻³⁰⁰ ✓

4) I want a refund on my ⚹ quad bike insurance. ✓

5) I want my quad bike to work as normal when accelerating. ✓

6) I want all thieving suspicions ⚹ cleared of me. ✓

7) I want a terraced house for a good price in a good area. ✓

… And How They Came True

☆☆☆☆

4) A quad bike insurance return was given to me.

5) My quad bike was working OK on a test run the other week.

6) I want to sell my quad bike.

3) Gave laptop to parents. Non applicable.

2) Decided not to pursue.

My List of Wishes

☆☆☆☆

1) I wish for my Dovolo Dlan kue to work. ✓

2) I want another job that works for me. ✓

3) I want to sell my Download ticket successfully to Pete.

9/6/08

4)